CREEPY CASTLES

Contents

Sir Bold and the Haunted Castle	page 2
Castles	page 14

Diana Bentley
and Sylvia Karavis

Story illustrated by
Tom Percival

Before Reading

In this story

 Sir Bold
 Hal
 Flash

Tricky words

- notice
- about
- ghosts
- castle
- stairs
- bedroom

Introduce these tricky words and help the reader when they come across them later!

Story starter

Sir Bold was a poor knight who lived long ago. He had a faithful servant called Hal and an old horse called Flash. One day, they saw a notice about a castle for sale.

Sir Bold and the Haunted Castle

Sir Bold read the notice.

"I want that castle," said Sir Bold.

"What about the ghosts?" said Hal.

"There are no ghosts," said Sir Bold.

They went up to the castle. It was very old.
"There are ghosts here," said Hal.

Sir Bold and Hal went into the castle.
They saw some food.
The food had gone bad.

"I don't like it here," said Hal. "I don't like the ghosts."

"Don't be silly," said Sir Bold. "There are no ghosts here."

Sir Bold and Hal went up the stairs.
The stairs were very old.

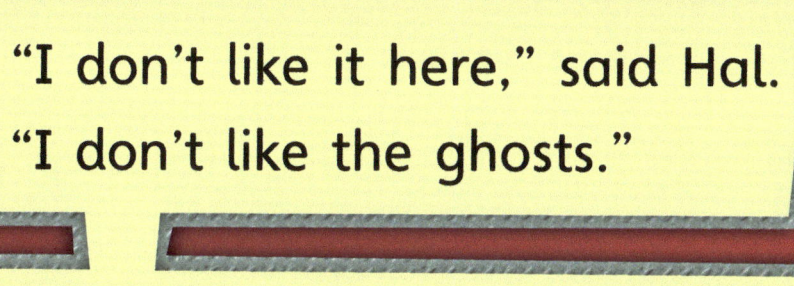

"I don't like it here," said Hal. "I don't like the ghosts."

"Don't be silly," said Sir Bold. "There are no ghosts here."

They went in the bedroom. "There are no ghosts here," said Sir Bold.

WHOOOOOOOOOO!

"Aaargh!" said Sir Bold. "There **are** ghosts here!"

Sir Bold and Hal ran away.

"I don't want that castle now," said Sir Bold.
"I don't like the ghosts!"

Quiz

Text Detective

- Why do you think the castle was cheap?
- Why do you think Sir Bold didn't buy the castle?

Word Detective

- **Phonic Focus:** Blending three phonemes
  Page 12: Can you sound out 'ran'?
  What sound is in the middle?
- Page 6: Find a word rhyming with 'mood'.
- Page 9: Find a word that means 'foolish'.

Super Speller

Read these words:

here   old   said

Now try to spell them!

HA! HA! HA!

Q: When do ghosts eat breakfast?
A: In the moaning.

Before Reading

Find out about

- How knights kept enemies out of their castles

Tricky words

- castle
- knights
- enemies
- towers
- drawbridge
- moat

Introduce these tricky words and help the reader when they come across them later!

Text starter

Many castles were built nearly 1000 years ago. They had thick walls, strong doors, a drawbridge and a moat to stop enemies getting into the castle.

Castles

Look at this castle.
It is high up on a hill.
From the hill, knights could see enemies coming to the castle.

Look at this castle.
It is not on a high hill, but it has very high towers.

From the high towers, knights could see enemies coming to the castle.

Look at this castle.

It has a strong drawbridge.

A strong drawbridge stopped enemies getting into the castle.

Look at this castle.
It has a moat around it.
The moat has water in it.

A moat stopped enemies getting into the castle. Enemies could not get across the water.

How did a moat stop the enemies?

Look at this castle.
This castle has very thick walls.
The thick walls stopped enemies getting into the castle.

Castle windows were very thin.

Knights could shoot arrows **out** of the castle, but …
enemies could not shoot arrows **into** the castle!

Castle doors were very strong. The strong doors stopped enemies getting into the castle.

Castles were very strong.
The enemies have gone, but …
the castles are still there.

Quiz

Text Detective

- Why were castle windows thin?
- Would you like to have lived in a castle?

Word Detective

- **Phonic Focus:** Blending three phonemes
  Page 16: Can you sound out 'not'?
  What is the sound in the middle?
- Page 21: Why is the word 'out' in bold?
- Page 21: Find a word to rhyme with 'boot'.

Super Speller

Read these words:

into   look   hill

Now try to spell them!

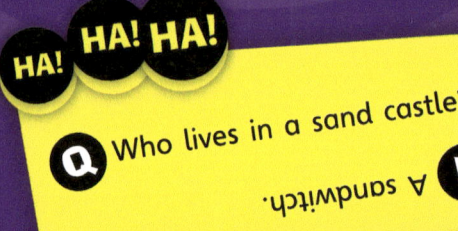

HA! HA! HA!

Q Who lives in a sand castle?

A A sandwitch.